Six Days in Iceland

Alyson Hallett travelled to Iceland as poet in residence with the University of Exeter's geography department in Cornwall (funded by the Leverhulme Trust). She has published short stories, drama and an audio-diary for BBC Radio 4 and runs an international poetry-as-public-art project, *The Migration Habits of Stones*. Her latest book of poems is *The Stone Library* (Peterloo Poets).

Chris Caseldine is Professor of Quaternary Environmental Change at the University of Exeter, Cornwall Campus. He first visited Iceland in 1975, researches into glacial and climate change and has been taking student fieldtrips to the country since 1979. He has written 31 papers and co-edited 2 books on Iceland: *Environmental Change in Iceland: Past and Present* and *Iceland — Modern Processes and Past Environments*.

Sam Inglis and Francesca Clark are full-time students studying BSc Geography at the University of Exeter, Cornwall Campus. Anna Caseldine is a full-time student of English Literature at Cardiff University.

Six Days in Iceland

Foreword: Catherine Leyshon
Poems: Alyson Hallett
Photographs: Anna Caseldine, Francesca Clark, Alyson Hallett, Sam Inglis
Text: Chris Caseldine

Dropstone Press 2011

This book is dedicated to Germán Dates, 1941–2011
Mapmaker in the Andes, Argentina

In Icelandic we don't talk about cultivating the soil — we say *ad yrkja jördina*. The verb *ad yrkja* means to write poetry. When we put seeds into the soil we therefore tend to think of it as making poems from the soil. We are making poetry of the land. We are writing the land. And when we pick flowers we call it *ad lesa blóm*. The verb *lesa* means to read. We are reading the flowers.

Gudmundur Andri Thorsson

Foreword

In 1946, the president of the Association of American Geographers, John K Wright, addressed the audience of the forty third annual meeting in Columbus, Ohio, on the place of imagination in geography. Years before the humanistic turn would legitimate research on subjectivities and imaginaries in geography, Wright spoke compellingly of how a fundamentally emotional and embodied attraction to landscape moves even the most scientific geographers. He recalled the poetic spell induced by the view from the top of a mountain, then went on to urge geographers to admit imaginative and poetic responses to the landscape into their work and resist the temptation to treat the scientific and aesthetic as separate and incompatible realms of knowing:

> Thus, with all due respect toward those who may think differently, I do not regard the scientific and the aesthetic either as mutually exclusive or as antagonistic in geography. Repression of the poetic in our imaginative faculties may deprive us of much of the satisfaction that geographical studies could otherwise yield and render our teaching and writing less powerful than they might well be.

It took another sixty-four years before the first poet in residence in a UK Geography department, Alyson Hallett, was appointed, from September 2010 to May 2011. Funded by the Leverhulme Trust, Alyson's aim was to challenge and augment her own understanding of landscape and at the same time, introduce physical and human geography students and staff at the University of Exeter's Cornwall Campus to an imaginative, poetic appreciation of landscape which exceeded the geographical canon, making the familiar objects of our geographical enquiries unfamiliar. She often questioned our established epistemologies and nurtured an appreciation of the inherent poetry of geographical language, scientific lexicon and landscape's idiom.

During the residency, Alyson was keen to investigate what kinds of exchanges might occur between a poet and a scientist. She explored, through conversations with students and lecturers, the similarities and differences in the ways in which poets and scientists read and respond to landscapes. Some undergraduates were taken by surprise when Alyson delivered a poem at the beginning of lectures on National Poetry Day, but staff, postgraduates and students alike quickly began to enjoy and participate in Alyson's poetic interventions. These included geopoetic lunches, a creative writing group, and poetry which appeared overnight on walls, office doors and windows.

Alyson's residency culminated in her participation in the Iceland fieldtrip, when she accompanied a group of second year geography undergraduates led by Professor Chris Caseldine. This volume has arisen from the fieldtrip and is one of the outcomes of the residency. The juxtaposition of Alyson's poems, Chris' scientific prose and photographs by Sam Inglis, Francesca Clark, Anna Caseldine (students on the trip) and Alyson, destabilises our expectations of what a geography of Iceland might be like. An emotional and intuitive engagement with landscape threads through Chris' text while the poetry of geomorphology, process and deep geological memory infuses Alyson's verses. Through poetry, image and text, Iceland's landscapes become magical yet complex, majestic yet intimate.

Six Days in Iceland is an act of witnessing Iceland that examines the observers' innate natures as well as the nature of the environment. It contributes to the ways in which we experience and articulate the mutuality of engagement between geographer and landscape by focusing attention on the language we employ to talk about landscape. The inclusion of imagination, dream and memory inspires a new awareness of our relationship with landscapes that are experienced as dynamic and co-creative.

Catherine Leyshon
Associate Professor of Historical and Cultural Geography
University of Exeter, Cornwall Campus
June 2011

Renaissance Hotel, Heathrow

In the hotel lobby
a piece of mica-sparkled rock
sits on a silver platter
behind the check-in counter

like the head of John the Baptist

only it wasn't Salome who danced for the prize
it was an Icelandic volcano

a reminder, the receptionist says,
of last year's eruption.

Swimming Pool, Reykjavík, 1st April

At a temperature of one degree
we see our breath in air

steam rises from geothermal pools
the water sees its breath too

April in Iceland

Resurrection: dead grass reconsiders life
redwings arrive

snow scripts the hills
a language hewn out of ice

the sun's handwriting
spill of white

redwings unflinching
as people pass by —

April in Iceland

Land
bare and recently unbandaged

Unsnowed

Migrating geese knackered after working their wings
against the jet-stream

Food in the field

Continents of cloud shadow
passing over the mountains

Going on to pass over the sea

We meet whatever we need to meet

The moment when a car, bus, cyclist and two running dogs cross paths
the road otherwise empty for hundreds of miles

The moment when stones look down as we look up
Law Rock, one stone clasped like a jewel at the top

The moment when a town issues a sudden apology for existing
each building an excuse-me for its brief appearance

The moment when snow melts and carries away a road
when geysers publish their skyward bulletins

The moment when nothing seems to grow on the maddening plains
a few horses, a house, a pylon

And then those two swans flying over, banking to the right
four white wings beating air —

Thinking of Iceland

Chris counsels us to think of Iceland as flat

even the mountains are flat, he says,
when you see them as layer upon layer of lava

generations of flatness
inhabited by trolls

outcrops of horizontalled time

then he counsels us to think south not north
to unhitch the island from a European mind
connect it with the Arctic's
southern-most tip

we place ourselves there, the sea's currents
fat with cod, herring,
radioactivity from decommissioned warships.

X

Five whooper swans fly by
and we ask
where is the one who is missing?

Night, Iceland

I walk away from the hotel

move through these last luminous moments
four stones by the path
the bar's yellowish light glancing off the track

and then I am gone

into the sound of water
into darkness so complete it undoes me

one or two stars collapse through a cloud
then disappear

my head fills with absence —

I watch the thousand thoughts clamber into the past
and say they must stay there now,
he is not coming back

and when it's too much I return to
the constant traffic of water
the snow-washed air

breathe it in until I am
snow-washed too —

Deforming

deforming ice pours
down a mountain's
side

movement
melt
changes of shape

the geographer's tongue
as clean
as the substance it talks about

Atlas of Iceland in Nineteen Pages

for Germán Dates

p.1

I move a stone and everything changes —
me, the stone,
the earth that held the stone
water that runs through earth
root of birch
mash of moss
lichen

the map undulates across this frozen land —

behind us, in the retreating ice,
two dead bodies are waiting
to be delivered —

p.2

They say a glacier gives back
the things it takes

that it will not hold them forever

p.3

So far this one, at Skaftafell, has given the remains of a tent,
2 backpacks, 1 pair of trousers, 1 pair of socks,
ski bindings, wood from the skis,
pan and handle,
hammer head, crampons, goggles, spanner,
toothbrush

It has not yet
given Ian Harrison and Tony Prosser —
students from Nottingham University
doing fieldwork in 1953

It has so far refused
to relinquish their bodies.

p.4

If they come they will be midwifed by sun

the sun's heat winnowing ice
to water

and

they will be midwifed by movement

deforming ice
pouring down the mountain
like treacle

p.5

Francesca says
What if Katla explodes while we're here
What if a flood comes down off the mountain
What if we can't escape

p.6

No brake strong enough
to stop the flood —

here, in the clean air of the mountains
we learn that we are able to die —

p.7

The stone dies to the life it was leading
each time we move it

the day dies each time the light falls away

each learning of dying
presses us into the passion of life

this breath, this urgent now

p.8

We will all grow old in different ways

bodies in ice

whooper swans
who mate for life

moss
stones, moraines

the northern lights will grow old
and the young lava that comes to cover land
will be made of old things rekindled in fire

these maps, these gyres of place, position, elevation
are already out of date —

the sun is coming upon the mountain

the ice is deforming

a single duck, then raven, flies over.

p.9

You cannot mistake the shape of the glacier
when seen from above — a tongue, a white tongue

it pours down the mountain
It creaks as it moves

and soon this melt will spell something new
into the language of its body.

p.10

Flood is another word
for the music of water.

p.11

Out here in this clean air
by this high mountain
with swan-white snow
the sound of melting ice
like the sound stars might make if we could hear them

Out here where the great black plains
stretch for miles to the sea
five swans
then five geese fly by

Out here surrounded by ice and stone
the dead stalks
of lupins and the glance
of cloud-muted light, out here
I can say who I am

p.12

Yes
I am frightened

Yes
I am full of dread

Yes the land is indifferent
to its warm-blooded guests

p.13

Stuck to a stone
my bones sore from sitting for so long.

Who knows what we will take home from here?

Measurements, samples, data, stones,
stories of volcanic eruptions, eruptions of our own.

p.14

Heat percolates beneath the ice
mountains hide inside the earth

a future of unerupted lava
waits inside the volcano —

p.15

Seen from above
the ice field is a tongue.

There are no fields in Iceland.
There is land and farms and barns.

p.16

They say the glacier gives back
everything it takes. Our footsteps, then,
are included in its inventory,
the dig of crampons, the reverberating step,
sound waves of our voices.

All of these have been taken into the house of blue ice.

p.17

One day the glacier
will give everything back.

This is said, not written,
and sayings are as fluid as water itself.

p.18

We are not so different, we and our world,
nature massed as moss on stone,
maps, measurements, an atlas of moraines

these readings of land a reading of ourselves.

p.19

In the library of fire and water
we are all forming and deforming
brittle bones
brittle rocks

only the spirit plastic enough to unstitch time.

Out here, surrounded by mountains…

Out here, surrounded by mountains, glaciers, plains that stretch to the sea, I wonder what it means to find myself surrounded by so much space, as if all this immensity is, in some way, changing me.

Seeing a car drive along the road is an event. Two or three cars and we wonder why it is so busy.

The swans are loud as they fly over, honking, the rush of air against their wings. They gain height in the sky, thirteen in this group, one trailing behind. Chris thinks they might be preparing to cross the mountains and head further north.

Lambs will not be born here until late April. Halldor, our bus driver, will help his brother with lambing this year. His other brother died last year. I tell him I have helped with lambing. That as a child, every summer, we went to my uncle's farm, hay-making and milking at dawn. You have done this? Halldor says. Did you like? Yes, I say, it was good, it gave me a feeling for life.

Later, walking alone by the glacier, I realise that the land I lived in as a child is so deeply etched inside I can still smell it.

It is the air and the earth and the animals and the insects and the people and the culture who define who I am.

If I am a poet I am also a tree, a heron, a cow, a deformed lamb, a deforming glacier, a tractor, mist on the moors at dawn.

Everything is music when you think like that. Even the lamb's afterbirth is a note on the scale.

We are frequently serenaded by swans here. Whooper swans. My mother's maiden name is Hooper: the spelling is different but the sound is the same. There is Hooper blood in my veins. Carolina, a friend from Santiago, Chile, once told me I reminded her of a swan.

It is perhaps true that I mated for life. That love was lost a long time ago. Since then, I have been a roving widow.

The swans are flying at least as fast as the bus. 90km per hour. Naomi tells me the bones in their wings are hollow, that they are strengthened with crossways struts.

Today I saw blue ice in the sea.

I keep looking in the mirror and asking, is this still me?

Reflection

There are glaciers in my eyes
they've come home with me
bluewhite, wavelets and canyons

They advance and retreat
keep company with the luminous dark
this dance of water

Iceland Island

Yes it was frightening there.
It was young there, hidden, raw, like being in the mouth
of a lion.

Ice so luminous, there on the black beach,
it was creaturely, alive
as it pursued its path to the sea.

Land of fire: fire underfoot,
underpeak, under-ice
water boiling out of the earth.

Never tasted air like that:
sometimes sulphur, sometimes so fresh my lungs turned blue
and pinned their flags to the mountains.

Flood

And it all begins with that sound
in Spring

drops falling off
the glacier's edge

an echo of music
waiting to be played.

1

The nature of the Icelandic physical landscape is largely driven by horizontality. Over its short geological history Iceland has been built up by successive outpourings of lava (now largely seen as horizontally bedded basalts) sandwiching remains of former glacial deposits left by ice sheets and ice caps of various size. These glacial deposits are known as tillites; glacial sediments or tills that have been lithified due to the burial under later strata. Both the volcanic activity and the glaciers leave deposits that are spread over former landscapes. In the absence of any deformation by processes commonly found away from the spreading margins of tectonic plates — the sort of disruption commonly seen in Europe which leads to the formation of mountain ranges such as the Alps — the strata are at best gently dipping as they move away from the eruption centres. Because of the action of ice and rivers the horizontal strata are cut by deeply incised glacial and fluvial valleys. This reveals the past at the surface and allows us to interpret the geological history of the island.

Some deposits do not adhere to such simple rules: the main shield volcanoes form much more extensive features akin to the classical cone-shaped volcanoes, vertical rock strata known as dikes can be seen in cliff faces, where molten magma forced its way through surrounding rocks, and occasional masses of disturbed rock disrupt a hillside where large rockfalls have taken place, often triggered by earthquakes. Where eruptions occurred under the ice there are more amorphous masses of rock left as a result of the mix of magma and melted ice, known technically as hyaloclastites, producing some of the weirder rock formations to be found in Iceland.

This layered structure encapsulates recent geological time in a startlingly available manner. The oldest rocks in Iceland outcrop in the extreme east and west and date to around 15 million years ago, well before the first glaciers appeared. They comprise lavas flowing over a landscape produced under much warmer conditions than those of the present. There are fossils of trees such as *Sequoia* and plants including vines in the oldest layers, reflecting the presence of deciduous forests now found in Eastern North America. The first evidence for ice on Iceland is seen in the form of the tillites, representing local glaciations beginning around 3.8 million years ago. This was before the Earth moved into the most recent major geological Era, the Quaternary, around 2.7 million years ago. From this time much larger ice caps covered the country and at least 20 different glacial phases have been identified overall. The pattern of glacial episodes and their dating provides a valuable terrestrial signal to compare to the undisturbed sequences found in adjacent deep sea sediments. These records show the changing temperatures of the ocean and hence changes in global temperatures. What this amazing geological record also represents is the increasing importance and extent of ice over Iceland as we get nearer, geologically, to the present day.

The burial of landscapes in Iceland continues to the present. Since the end of the last glacial period and over the current Holocene period that started 11,700 years ago, there have been at least 3 major ourpourings of lava in the form of flood basalts. 7,500 years ago the Þjórsá lava covered 950km^2 of southern Iceland, the largest lava flow on Earth since the end of the last glacial period. Shortly after the first Norse settlement in AD874 the Eldgjá lava covered 800km^2 and in 1783–84 the Laki eruption produced a further 580km^2 of lava, often covering the previous Eldgjá lava field. This latter event was graphically described by Jón Steingrímsson, a minister in Kirkjubæjarklaustur, a settlement threatened from both the east and west by the lava, "[t]he liquid fire poured forth over the land so that everything became mixed together".

The last millennium of volcanic activity can also be seen within the ice caps. On the Vatnajökull ice cap, the successive ash layers laid on the ice and trapped between snow, are now emerging as the ice melts near the terminus of several outlet glaciers. Thus by walking up the ice it is possible to step back in time through the eruption history of the neighbouring volcanoes. With the latest eruption of Grimsvötn, this whole ice surface has been covered by dark volcanic ash, but with the summer surface melt this will soon disappear, only surviving high up on the ice cap where it is buried by snow.

The present landscape in Iceland owes its form not only to constant burial by lava flows and ice, but also to the exhumation of these former surfaces. Recent soundings below the southern margin of the Vatnajökull ice cap under the glacier Breiðamerkurjökull have revealed a 20km long, 300m deep incipient fjord hidden beneath the ice. At present this terminates in the famous glacial lagoon Jökulsárlón. This lies a few hundred metres from the Atlantic, a distance shrinking by around 8m every year. With accelerating loss of the glacier it is possible to foresee the opening up of this fjord as the century progresses, which will result in ice calving directly into the sea. This in turn will lead to an even more rapid loss of ice.

All the major Icelandic glaciers lie on active volcanoes covering the central craters or calderas. With the eruption of Eyjafjallajökull in 2010 the caldera was revealed and a new lake formed as the magma cooled. This offsets the infilling of the lake in front of Gigjökull that lay along the route of the main glacial flood, or jökulhlaup, that derived from the eruption. The new caldera lake is already snow covered: the return to ice is therefore taking place as the central part of the ice cap rebuilds.

There are a number of lakes hidden beneath the large Vatnajökull ice cap. Several of these periodically fill because of geothermal heat beneath the ice, and then catastrophically drain in a matter of hours as short, high intensity jökulhlaups. These glacial floods have the power to move rocks the size of houses, often leaving them stranded on the extensive flat outwash plains that stretch out beyond the margins of the glaciers.
During the Little Ice Age, the time between the 15th century and the end of the 19th or beginning of the 20th century, Vatnajökull overran farms around its southern margin. As the ice now retreats we may expect over the coming century to see remains of some of these reappear. However these remains will not be recognisable as houses or fields. Given the pressure of the ice and the abundant meltwater any evidence will be at best fragmentary.

Ice is a plastic substance, although this is not obvious from the apparently brittle nature of a crevassed glacier surface. Ice deforms and creeps and moves as much by deformation as by sliding or slipping. In Iceland where glaciers are defined as temperate, they have a 'warm' base due to the pressure melting of ice as it overlies the surface over which it flows. There are indeed some glaciers that are actually known as 'cold' because they are frozen to their bed, but not in Iceland.

Much of our understanding of the nature of ice and how it moves derives from studies in the Alps in the middle of the 19th century as series of scientists from different countries sought to observe and explain glacial phenomena. James Forbes in 1843 described glaciers as "…a granular compound of ice and water, possessing, under certain circumstances, …a rude flexibility sensible even to the hand".

Ironically an Icelander, Sveinn Pálsson, variously a school teacher, farmer, fisherman and doctor who spent his summers in the late 18th century travelling around Iceland observing the landscape, had already written a *Treatise on Glaciers* in 1795. In this he compared ice to pitch, "…partly liquid like various kinds of resin". His work was sent to the colonial capital in Denmark, then on to Norway where it was locked away and forgotten, only being published in 1945, a century after others such as Forbes, Agassiz and Tyndall had achieved academic recognition for 'discovering' the properties of ice and glacier flow.

When the remains of the camp and equipment belonging to the lost members of the 1953 University of Nottingham expedition appeared on the surface of Skaftafellsjökull in July 2006, they not only provided a poignant reminder of what had happened half a century before, but also reinforced our scientific understanding that whatever a glacier takes in it will eventually relinquish. As yet no bodies have been traced in the ice, probably because they died on a different part of the ice cap trying to make it back to low ground. The possibility remains that they may, like Ötzi the iceman found in the Austrian Alps, have sought refuge in a sheltered spot not connected to ice moving off the mountain and hence will only be discovered by chance by mountaineers in a future world with less ice. As the location of the original camp could be pinpointed, it has been possible to use the movement of the remains to estimate the rate at which ice moves within the glacier. All the remains were found within a very small area, only 100m in diameter, showing they travelled 8.5kms in 53 years. This gives a rate of movement, or ice velocity, of 0.4–0.5m per day, quite fast for a glacier but one that proved very similar to estimates that had been made on the basis of the local climate and general characteristics of Skaftafellsjökull.

Glaciers are divided into two units separated by an imaginary line known as the Equilibrium Line. Above this line the glacier accumulates, below it melts or ablates; above it grows, below it declines. This simple distinction also governs another important feature of glaciers: accumulation leads to movement into the ice, which means that anything taken up by ice (including rocks and bodies) will flow into it, melting leads to movement out of the ice. Hence the remains could only reappear below the Equilibrium Line. Moraines, the dumps of rocks and sediments excavated and transported by the ice, can similarly only be formed around the lower limits of the ice, they do not appear at higher levels where snow and ice accumulate.

In order to understand how glaciers change over time it is also necessary to reconcile what happens to the ice itself. Ice flows from high to low ground, not only due to gravity but also to a range of forms of deformation, thus ice is always 'advancing' in this sense. At the same time below the Equilibrium Line ice is being lost as it melts, especially during the summer season. The ice front may be retreating because the loss is greater than the rate with which the replacement ice can travel. In southern Iceland ice moves at relatively high velocities. Along the coast precipitation is very high, possibly as much as 10m of snow per year on the highest parts of the Öræfajökull ice cap. With such a large input of snow the glaciers are very dynamic and respond quickly to change. Since the end of the Little Ice Age, here probably the later decades of the 19th century, ice fronts have retreated, for Svínafellsjökull by over 1km. This did not take place at a constant rate of retreat. In the 1960s–80s cooler conditions allowed some cessation of decay and even ice advance. This change was driven by a cooling in the North Atlantic known as the Great Salinity Anomaly, when cold fresh water from Greenland and the Arctic appeared around Iceland. Although it did not last for long, it allows us to begin to understand the likely effect any future accelerated melting of Greenland would have on the ocean and on the surrounding land areas. With any climate warming that melts Greenland ice the first sign in Iceland and Europe will be an increase in cold as the North Atlantic cools. Over the last two decades retreat has again become the norm and is predicted to accelerate over the 21st century. The only way the glaciers could keep their present size in a warmer world would be to get more snow but it is difficult to see how this could happen, especially when precipitation levels are already so high.

5

Looking from western Europe Iceland is definitely north, yet there is still a lot of latitude to go, as much as 25°. The Arctic Circle barely touches the northernmost part of Iceland, the island of Grímsey off the north coast. Thus from the perspective of the Arctic Iceland is very much south, and Icelanders need to look to the north for all sorts of reasons. Pack ice is brought down from northern Greenland and the high Arctic by the East Greenland Current. It laps onto the northern coast of Iceland, occasionally expanding both east and west, in rare years near encircling the island. Over the last century the incidence of drift ice has been much reduced, but during the height of the Little Ice Age it impacted severely on life. Travelling in Hornstrandir in NW Iceland in 1886 the geologist Thorvaldur Thoroddsen wrote:

> The drift-ice had penetrated close in to the shore. The fjords and glens were shrouded in the cold fogs which generally accompany the drift-ice. All August it snowed and rained without intermission; …We used up all the provisions we had brought with us, and for several weeks had to live upon half-decayed seafowl, shark's flesh, and such like delicacies of the native inhabitants of the region.

In scientific terms drift ice, which would commonly be seen as icebergs, has provided very useful insights into some major environmental shifts over recent geological time — the last few million years. During the height of glacial periods when a large ice sheet covered northern North America, this ice mass periodically collapsed and 'armadas' of icebergs flooded into the North Atlantic. We know this because dropstones, pebbles released from the icebergs as they melted crossing the ocean, can be found in the sediments on the ocean floor. As you get further away from America the material gets finer and finer until it can only be seen microscopically. It is however possible to look at the chemistry of this material and determine exactly where it came from, as this is determined by the geology over which the ice passed. When Icelandic ice was lost into the sea around the island — and during glacial periods ice extended well beyond the present coastal margins — it too provided dropstones and fine sediments that ended up in the Atlantic sediments, identifiable on the basis of the very distinctive volcanic geology of the island.

Iceland lies across one of the main outlets of the largely landlocked Arctic Ocean so anything entering the ocean north of Russia may find its way south around the Icelandic coast. This includes useful items such as driftwood, prized in earlier times for building houses and ships, as well as less welcome material such as nuclear waste associated with the sinking of Soviet naval vessels in the Arctic Ocean north of Russia. The drift ice has also brought with it polar bears, useful in providing highly valued skins for export in earlier times, but now killed immediately on landfall to protect the sparsely settled areas around the northwest in particular. The latest traveller appeared in May 2011 and there seems to have been something of an upsurge in numbers over recent years.

Iceland is both a resting ground and destination point for birds migrating across the north Atlantic. Whooper swans arrive in early spring from their wintering grounds in Britain and mainland Europe. Their journey varies from 24 hours to several days, and they can be seen landing along the southern coast before their brief but perilous final leg across the ice cap to breeding grounds in northern and western Iceland. Various species of geese similarly stop-over in southern and western Iceland before heading further afield to their breeding areas in Greenland.

References

Thorsson, Gudmundur, A. (2009) Writing and Reading the Land. *Topos* 69: 98–9.

Wright, John K. (1947) Terrae Incognitae: The Place of Imagination in Geography. *Annals of the Association of American Geographers* 37: 1–15.

Forbes, J.D. (1843) *Travels through the Alps of Savoy and Other Parts of the Pennine Chain with Observations on the Phenomena of Glaciers.* Edinburgh: Adam and Charles Black; London: Longman, Brown, Green, and Longmans.

Pálsson, S. (2004) *Draft of a Physical, Geographical, and Historical Description of Icelandic Ice Mountains on the Basis of a Journey to the Most Prominent of Them in 1792–1794, with Four Maps and Eight Perspective Drawings.* Edited and translated by Richard S. Williams, Jr., and Oddur Sigurðsson, Icelandic Literary Society.

Steingrímsson, J. (1998) *Fires of the Earth. The Laki Eruption 1783–1784.* University of Iceland Press.

Thoroddsen, T. (1899) Explorations in Iceland during the years 1881–1898. *The Geographical Journal* 12: 251–274, 480–513.

Photographs

35. Mossfellsheiði (S.I.)
36. Svínafellsjökull (A.H.)
37. Öræfi (S.I.)
38. Whooper swans flying towards Vatnajökull (F.C.)
39. Bridge across Skeiðarársandur (A.H.)
40. Svínafellsjökull (S.I.)
41. Svínafellsjökull ice front (A.H.)
42. Ice from Jökulsárlón on the beach (A.H.)
43. Looking north from Reykjavík (S.I.)
44. Mýrdalssandur (A.H.)
45. Looking north from Reykjavík (S.I.)
46. Ice from Jökulsárlón on the beach (A.H.)
47. Bridge by Jökulsárlón (A.H.)
48. View west from Dyrhólaey (A.C.)

Acknowledgements

We would like to thank the following Geography BSc students for their enthusiastic participation in the 2011 fieldtrip to Iceland from the Tremough Campus in Cornwall:

Francesca Clark, William Cunnington, Dominic Flint, George Garrett, Richard Gregory, Oliver Haydon, Saskia Henney, Thea Humphrey, Samuel Inglis, Catrin Jones, Mark Nunns, Megan Rowe, Harriet Skinner, Peter McGaul, Terence Matthews, Julian Templeton, Robin Watson.

Thanks to Naomi Holmes, Halldor Þorsteinsson and Anna Caseldine.
Thanks also to Caroline Carver, Jan Nowell and Penelope Shuttle.

We acknowledge with thanks the following supporters of this publication:

The Leverhulme Trust. Alyson was supported by an Artist in Residence grant from the Leverhulme Trust (F/00 144/BO). These awards are intended to support the residency of an artist of any kind or nationality in a UK institution in order to foster a creative collaboration between the artist and the staff and/or students of that institution. The scheme is intended to bring artists into research and study environments where creative art is not part of the normal curriculum or activities of the host department.

The Geographies of Creativity and Knowledge Research Group of the Department of Geography, University of Exeter. Special thanks to Professor John Wylie, the research group leader, for his support.

The Leverhulme Trust

First published in 2011
Dropstone Press
Westerley, Vicarage Road
Stoke Gabriel, Totnes, Devon TQ9 6QP

ISBN 978 0 9569940 0 4
Designed and produced by Colin Sackett